Eating Hints

Recipes and Tips for Better Nutrition
During Cancer Treatment

U.S. DEPARTMENT OF HEALTH AND HUMAN SERVICES
Public Health Service
National Institutes of Health

National Cancer Institute
Bethesda, Md. 20205

NIH Publication No. 80-2079
Reprinted August 1980

Table of Contents

Dedicated to the 99 people

who took the time to share their experiences

so that others might benefit

Some Words About This Book

The Office of Cancer Communications, National Cancer
Institute, is pleased to reprint this book which was written by
members of the Yale-New Haven Medical Center—Marion E.
Morra, Communications Director, Nancy Suski, dietitian and
Bonny L. Johnson, Oncology Nurse. The book was written
to help cancer patients, their families and friends find ways to
eat well and to enjoy eating, particularly at those times when
cancer treatment or the disease itself causes problems.

The book is based on interviews with 99 cancer patients who
live in the New Haven, Connecticut, area. The authors report
that despite the different kinds of cancers and the different
treatments, eating problems experienced by these 99 patients
fell into five general categories—nausea and vomiting, loss
of appetite, mouth soreness and dryness, tired feeling and
intestinal upset. The information, advice, and helpful hints
for dealing with these problems were culled from discussions
with these patients and their families. There are also some
suggestions from members of the Yale School of Nursing
and the Connecticut Division of the American Cancer Society.

The recipes included have been chosen to help solve the
problems discussed. All of them are easy to prepare. Many are
old favorites which have been changed, adding extra protein
or other nutrients. All recipes have been taste-tested with
the help of the Regional Visiting Nurses Agency that serves
the New Haven area of Connecticut.

Why Is It Important To Eat Well When You Have Cancer?

We have all been told many times it is important for everybody to eat well. It is especially important for people with cancer.

Why?:

- Doctors and researchers have been finding that patients who eat well during their treatment periods — especially those who eat diets high in protein and calories — are better able to stand the side effects of the treatments, be they chemotherapy, radiation therapy, immunotherapy or surgery. Those who eat well may even be able to withstand a higher dose of certain treatments.

- A balanced diet can help maintain your strength, can prevent body tissues from breaking down and can help rebuild the normal tissues that have been affected by the treatments.

- Cancer patients with good eating habits can have fewer infections and be able to be up and about more.

- When you eat less, for whatever cause, your body uses its own stored up fat, protein and other nutrients, such as iron. Most cancer patients lose weight because they do not eat as much food as their body needs. Some patients do not eat because they are depressed. The disease or the treatments may reduce their appetites or unpleasant side effects of the treatment may cause them to eat less.

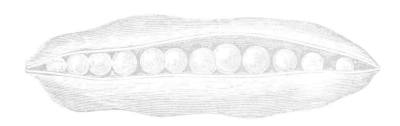

Some General Advice About Eating

Many of the people we talked with gave suggestions for dealing with the difficulties of eating. We asked about foods which people with cancer particularly like or dislike. Although in some cases the suggestions we received are generally known, we feel they are worth repeating since they are nutritionally sound and make good sense.

- **Give food a chance.** Remember that what sounds unappealing today may sound good tomorrow. An open-minded attitude of giving food a chance is the basis of this booklet. Try some of the suggestions and recipes that have worked for others. Experiment with different solutions.

- **Take advantage of the up times.** When you feel well, take advantage of it by eating well and by preparing meals which you can freeze for the down days. On the good days, eat when you feel hungry, even if it isn't mealtime. It is important to eat foods with good nutritional value, as many nutrients can be stored in your body for later use.

- **Discuss your eating problems with your doctor and your health team.** Before you try home remedies, be sure your problems are not symptoms needing medical attention. Do not hesitate to ask questions and to tell the doctor what seems to be bothering you even if you think it might seem unimportant.

- **Make use of timesavers.** Take advantage of time and effort-saving foods and appliances. That includes foods which can be prepared as a meal-in-a-dish with little preparation and cooking. Frozen dinners, when served with fruit, milk and buttered roll, can give you a sound nutritional meal. Some canned foods, such as soups, spaghetti sauce or gravies, can be mixed easily with fresh cooked meat for a good dinner. We have listed several hints under the sections titled *Hints for Adding Protein to Your Diet* and *Hints for Adding Calories to Your Diet.* Timesavers also mean appliances such as food processors, blenders and toaster ovens. There is information about choosing and using them in the section titled *Helpful Appliances.*

- **Atmosphere does make a difference.** An attractively set table with flowers or other such items can take your mind off a slumping appetite. Good odors also help — freshly baked bread or cakes baking. A glass of wine or beer before meals (with your doctor's approval) helps to relax you and can help to make you hungry. Eating with friends, having music at dinner time, varying the place in your house where you eat, having different

3

foods each day — even having a picnic at home — were all suggested. Most people also told us they enjoyed going out to eat in a restaurant for a change.

- **Avoid foods that don't interest you.** It was interesting to see that many of the people had omitted foods that were not particularly healthful. A third of the people told us that they no longer enjoyed potato chips, candy, alcoholic drinks, or fried foods. Most told us that these foods no longer tasted right or that they felt they were the cause of their nausea. Some of the vegetables that they no longer eat include cauliflower, corn, broccoli and beans because they produce bloating or gas. Many people lost their taste for coffee and tea or for red meat. On the other hand, people kept saying they liked those foods which were easy to eat and digest and have good nutritional value. For example, fresh fruits and vegetables were often mentioned as foods they particularly liked. Dishes made with pasta, milk products, eggs, fish and poultry lightly seasoned were also favorites.

- **Stay away from raw eggs and raw meats,** especially if your treatment or condition makes you susceptible to infection. (See the recipe for eggnog for a delicious one made with a cooked egg in a blender.)

General Eating Problems

Loss of appetite (or anorexia in medical terms) is a common complaint among people with cancer. Sometimes, treatments such as radiation or chemotherapy are the cause. But it also happens to people who are not having treatments. No one really knows what causes it — whether it is illness, pain, fatigue, stress, or depression or a combination of all of these. Some people say it happens once in a while, that their appetite comes and goes. Others tell us they rarely feel hungry. People say they eat less because they just aren't hungry, because food tastes either bad or just not right, because they have a bitter metal taste in their mouths or on their tongues, or because they simply get full too soon.

Are You Just Not Hungry?

- Try ice cream mixed with ginger ale or your favorite carbonated beverage as a drink. Or a milk shake or frozen yogurt.

- Eat small meals more often.

- Keep snacks handy for nibbling. It's been proven that people eat more when the food is easily available.

- Try eating a snack before you go to bed in addition to your other meals.

- Rely on food you really love during your not-hungry periods. Chicken soup and spaghetti with meatballs were both mentioned several times as favorites at this time.

- Look at the section titled *Hints For Adding Protein To Your Diet* for adding protein to foods without increasing the amount of foods you eat.

- Vary the color of foods served on the plate. Arrange it attractively. Add garnishes such as an orange slice, a slice of tomato or a sprig of parsley to make food more appealing.

- Concentrate on making your meal more enjoyable in every way with attractive settings, bright surroundings and good company. Soft music may help make mealtime more pleasant.

Has Your Taste For Some Foods Changed?

Some people have a bitter or a metallic taste in their mouth. Or a numbness in the mouth which blocks some tastes. Some people find they no longer enjoy the taste of red meat. Others tell us that sweet foods are harder to taste or that bitter foods taste stronger than before.

- If meat doesn't taste right, cook chicken, turkey or fish instead. Use eggs and dairy products as substitutes. Avoid fish which have a strong smell — cook on a barbecue if possible.

- Add bacon bits, sliced almonds, ham strips or pieces of onion to vegetables for added flavor.

- Tart foods may enhance flavors (especially for people who have no problems with their mouths or throats). Orange juice, pickles, lemonade, vinegar and lemon juice used as seasonings may help.

- Wines, beer or mayonnaise added to soups and sauces make them taste better. Chicken and fish can be added to cream soups for extra flavor and protein.

- Try marinating meat, chicken or fish in sweet fruit juices, sweet wines, Italian dressing, sweet-sour sauce for more taste. Use more and stronger seasonings such as basil, oregano, rosemary, tarregon, lemon juice or mint in your cooking.

- Many foods taste better if they are either cold or at room temperature.

- You can sometimes take away the strange taste in your mouth by drinking more liquids such as water, tea and ginger ale or by eating foods which leave their own tastes in your mouth, such as fresh fruits or hard candies.

- Be sure you have your dentist check your mouth and rule out dental problems causing bad taste. Ask about special mouthwashes and good mouth care.

6

Do You Find That You Feel Full When You've Only Eaten A Little Bit?

Almost half of the people we talked to told us they had this problem.

- Eat smaller meals more often. Keep nutritious snack foods around.

- Chew foods slowly — this prevents your stomach from becoming too full too quickly.

- Avoid greasy foods, butter and rich sauces.

- Make sure that the liquids you drink have nutritional content such as juices, milk shakes or milk.

- Don't drink liquids with your meals. Take them 30 to 60 minutes before your meals to reduce the volume of material in your stomach.

Problems With Nausea And Vomiting

The best news about the problems of nausea and vomiting caused by chemotherapy and radiation is that more than half of the patients we talked with never suffered from this complaint. For most of the people who did have the problem, it happened once in a while and was a temporary condition usually related to the treatments they were receiving. A few people seemed to have the problem with them almost all the time.

What Can Help You Eat While Nauseated Or Help Prevent Vomiting?

- Smaller portions of food that is low in fat seem to work — they are easier to digest and get through the stomach faster (see the section titled *Are You Looking For Foods Which Are Low In Fat?)* If you are eating smaller portions of low-fat foods, be sure to eat more often to make up for your calorie and protein needs.

- Eat salty foods and avoid overly sweet ones, especially if you have been vomiting.

- Eat dry foods such as toast or crackers, especially soon after getting up in the morning.

- If you know there are specific times when you are going to be nauseated or vomiting, don't eat foods you really like around these times because patients tell us that they were "turned off" by some of their favorite foods. They ate them during periods of nausea and vomiting and from that time on the foods became associated with the problem.

- Clear, cool beverages are recommended. Take whatever liquids you feel you can handle — clear soups, flavored gelatin, carbonated beverages (such as ginger ale), popsicles, ice cubes made of any kind of favorite liquid. Sip liquids slowly through a straw.

- Avoid liquids at mealtimes. Take them 30 to 60 minutes before eating.

- Do not lie down flat for at least two hours after eating. It may be helpful to rest after eating since activity can slow down digestion and increase your discomfort. If you wish to rest, sit down. If you recline make sure your head is at least 4 inches higher than your feet (you may want to put 4 inch blocks under the head of your bed).

- Sometimes loose clothing or fresh air can help.

- Ask the doctor for anti-nausea medicine if either nausea or vomiting symptoms are severe.

- If you are bloated, have pain or a swollen stomach before nausea and vomiting occur, and if these problems are relieved by vomiting, you should call the doctor.

Does Just The Smell Of Food Make You Nauseated?

Some people explained that even the smell of food cooking made them nauseated. There are several ways to help this problem.

- Let someone else do the cooking. Sit in another room or take a walk while the food is being cooked.

- Avoid foods or beverages that produce this effect, such as brewing coffee.

- Since greasy foods or fried foods seem to be the worst offenders, don't prepare fried foods during bad times.

- Use prepared foods from the freezer that can be warmed at a low temperature or a meal that doesn't need to be cooked.

Mouth and Throat Problems

The linings of the mouth and throat are among the most sensitive areas of the body. Cancer patients — especially those receiving chemotherapy or radiation treatments — often complain of soreness in these areas. These problems seem directly related to the treatment. Recent surgery in the head and neck area also may result in difficulty in chewing and swallowing. Remember that part of the healing process in this area of the body depends upon your eating well and drinking fluids.

- If you have mouth or throat problems, be sure to see your dentist.

- If you have sores under your dentures, do not wear them when you do not need them for eating. Check with your dentist.

- If your mouth is dry, ask the doctor whether the medicines you are taking are causing the dryness.

- If your gums, tongue and throat become dry or sore, follow the treatment prescribed by your doctor or nurse after you have discussed the problem with them.

Do You Have Trouble Chewing And/Or Swallowing Because Of Soreness Or Dryness?

- Try a softer diet. Use your favorite foods but make changes that will soften them.

- Use a blender. If you like vegetable soup, for example, heat then blend it. Food tastes better if it is cooked before it is blended. It is easier to blend warm food.

- Cut meats up in small pieces and add gravy to them. This also helps when you blend them.

- Use butter, gravies or cream sauces on meats and vegetables.

- Choose soft foods such as mashed potatoes, yogurt, scrambled or poached eggs, egg custards, ricotta cheese, milk shakes, puddings, gelatins, creamy cereals, macaroni and cheese.

- Make stews, casseroles and simmered foods, adding more liquids to make them softer.

- Use a little sugar to tone down acid or salty foods.

- Do not use hot spices such as pepper, chili powder, nutmeg and cloves. Avoid rough or coarse foods such as raw vegetables and bran.

- Don't eat dry foods like toast or hard breads unless you soak them. They can scratch delicate tissues.

- Eat your food lukewarm or cold rather than hot.

- Some people find cold foods can be soothing. If you do, add ice to milk and milk shakes for extra coldness. Eat ice cream and yogurt or make popsicles with milk or milk substitutes.

- Soak foods in coffee, tea, milk, cocoa or warm beverages.

- Most people find that citrus fruit juices and tomatoes sting or burn. Fruits that are low in acid, such as bananas or canned pears, are easier to swallow. So are peach, pear and apricot nectars and fruit drinks instead of fruit juice.

- Try tilting your head back or moving it forward to make swallowing easier.

- Use a straw or drink your food from a cup instead of using a spoon.

- Smoking and drinking certain alcoholic beverages can irritate your mouth and throat. Follow your doctor's advice.

- A humidifier or a steam kettle in the bedroom may help if your house is heated with dry heat.

- Rinse your mouth whenever you feel you need it (to remove debris, to stimulate your gums, to lubricate your mouth, or to put a fresh taste in your mouth).

- If needed, nutritional formulas can be used to provide adequate calories and nutrients.

- If your problem is severe, talk to your doctor about medicine to numb your gums and tongue or about artificial saliva or antifungal medication.

Feeling Tired

Almost everyone we talked with said he or she felt tired or fatigued at some point during the illness. As a matter of fact, feeling tired is normal for anyone with an illness. You may feel tired off and on for weeks following surgery as your body adjusts and recovers. Persons undergoing chemotherapy or radiation treatments (which affect normal tissues as well as tumor cells) often feel tired. In these settings of extensive tissue repair, you need both rest and good food. However, most people told us they do not feel like eating when they feel very tired. The solution most commonly offered was to rest first and eat later. Many times you'll feel more like eating after you have napped or rested.

What Can You Do When You Feel Too Tired To Eat?

Many people who are very tired may have a problem preparing and serving foods rather than eating it. This is the time to rely on the meals you have frozen when you felt well, or on convenience foods that are easy to prepare.

- Canned creamed soups make good tasting and nutritious sauces combined with fish or chicken and toast. Together with canned or fresh fruit, juices, or dairy foods, they make well-balanced and quickly prepared meals.

- If your tired feeling is related to your recovery from surgery or other treatments and you are gradually building up your strength, start by eating smaller portions of easily-digested foods and work slowly back to normal.

- If you find that you can pinpoint the times when you are the most tired, such as after you have a treatment, try to make and freeze meals ahead of time to use at this time.

- Accept the offers of friends to help you. Tell them what you need. People like to do things for others. Don't be embarrassed to ask for help and to accept and to direct your friends' aid.

- If you live alone, you might wish to arrange for "Meals On Wheels" to prepare your meals. Many communities offer this service. Contact your doctor, Visiting Nurses Association or American Cancer Society for information.

- If you feel tired when you wake up or if you are not sleeping at night, talk to your doctor. Do not take sleeping pills without the doctor's permission.

Problems With Diarrhea, Constipation, Bloating And Heartburn

There are several reasons for these problems to occur: certain tumors (such as those in the pancreas) and radiation therapy to the upper abdomen may affect your ability to digest and eliminate food normally. Some drugs such as pain medication may cause your bowel to slow down, resulting in constipation. Other drugs or radiation may irritate the intestines and cause loose bowel movements or diarrhea. Certain treatments and less activity may cause a bloated feeling or excessive gas. Cramps and diarrhea may result from treatment — the part of your intestine which breaks down lactose may be damaged. You may need to restrict your milk intake (if this happens see section titled *What Is Lactose Intolerance*).

Do You Ever Have Diarrhea Or Feel Like You Might Get It?

- Use less fiber (roughage) in your diet (roughage is the fibrous material in your food that you don't digest and is passed in bowel movements). If your intestines are irritated, the normal amount of fiber may be too much for them. Use only cooked fruits and vegetables, omitting those with seeds and tough skins, beans, broccoli, corn, onions, garlic, breads and nuts.

- Potassium is an important element to your body and is lost in great quantities when you have diarrhea. If you do not have enough potassium you can feel very weak. When you have diarrhea, make sure you eat some foods that are high in potassium (but that won't worsen the diarrhea) — such as bananas, apricot or peach nectar, fish, potatoes and meat. If you are unable to eat these foods talk to your doctor about taking potassium supplements.

- If you have cramps, stay away from foods that may encourage gas or cramps, such as carbonated drinks, beer, beans, cabbage, broccoli, cauliflower, highly spiced food, too many sweets and chewing gum.

- Stay away from fatty foods and foods which are highly spiced.

- Eat smaller amounts of food more often.

- Drink liquids between meals instead of with them. Make sure you drink plenty of liquids since diarrhea causes you to lose fluids and salts which you must replace.

- Do not skip meals. Try to chew with your mouth closed. Talking while you chew may cause you to swallow too much air which can cause gasiness or cramps.

- If your diarrhea is persistent or has blood in it, be sure to tell the doctor.

Do You Have Constipation, Hard Stools Or Trouble Moving Your Bowels?

Constipation can be a problem in people with cancer. It may result from treatment with some drugs. It can be a problem if you have been used to eating mostly soft and liquid foods.

- Your regular diet should include whatever has helped you move your bowels before, such as a variety of fruits and vegetables (twice a day), whole grain breads and cereals, dried fruits (raisins, prunes, or apricots), and nuts to add more fiber. If you cannot chew or swallow these, try grating them or putting them in a blender.

- Try adding one or two tablespoons of bran to your foods to keep regular. You can add it to cooked cereals, casseroles, eggs, in baked goods or eat it as a raw cereal.

- Try high-fiber snack foods such as sesame bread sticks, date nut bread, oatmeal cookies, fig newtons, date or raisin bars, granola, prune bread and corn chips.

- Drink plenty of liquids. Eight to ten full glasses each day are needed.

- Some patients drink prune juice or hot lemon water in the morning or at night. Hot liquids often stimulate bowel activity.

- Light exercise will sometimes help this problem.

- Set aside 10 to 30 minutes a day to quietly sit on the commode.

- If you are undergoing treatment, check with your doctor or nurse before taking a laxative and/or a stool softener.

Do You Ever Feel Bloated?

It would be difficult to name any one cause for the bloated feeling commonly reported. Certain foods may contribute to the production of air in the stomach or intestines. Less exercise may play a role. Some people say their problem is associated with radiation or chemotherapy. In addition, nervousness or rushed meals may cause you to swallow air as you eat.

- Eat foods that are easily digested, especially those that are bland or low in fat.

- Avoid foods which may cause gas formation such as onions, garlic and foods in the cabbage family.

- Try to eat more slowly — count to 10 while you are chewing each mouthful.

- Stop eating when you feel uncomfortable — take a walk or get a little exercise.

Do You Have Heartburn?

- Use mildly flavored seasoned foods, avoiding fried, greasy or heavily spiced ones. Eat smaller meals more often. They move more quickly through the stomach, helping to prevent heartburn.

- Don't lie down for two hours after eating. Elevate the head of the bed 4 inches.

- Take antacids one hour and three hours after meals, at bedtime and upon awaking in the middle of the night. If you take antacid, keep it chilled. It tastes better.

Are Your Problems With Diet Related To A Colostomy?

Most important for those who have a colostomy is to eat well-balanced meals. This is the best way to avoid diarrhea or constipation.

- If you think you might get constipated, drink more liquids and snack on dried fruits.

- To control gas, avoid foods like onions, cabbage, broccoli, corn, nuts and beer.

- If your colostomy squirts, call your doctor.

How Much Protein And How Many Calories Do I Need?

The needs will differ for each person. However, there are several basic facts which can help you:

- Protein and calorie needs are greater during illness, treatment and recovery than they normally are.

- Maintaining your weight is a good way to decide whether or not you are getting enough calories each day.

- Protein needs are more rigid than calorie needs. Therefore, your diet should emphasize protein.

- Daily needs for proteins and calories for healthy adults (U.S. Recommended Dietary Allowances) are 2,700 calories and 56 grams of protein for men; 2,000 and 45 grams of protein for women. During illness, treatment and recovery, 90 grams of protein for men and 80 grams of protein for women plus an additional 200 to 300 calories are recommended.

- You may want to record what you are getting in calories and protein. The recipes in this book list both calories and protein.

- For other foods you eat, you can get simple calorie guides in most department or discount stores or you can ask the dietary staff at your own hospital for help.

Hints For Adding Protein To Your Diet

You can add protein to your diet without increasing the amount of food you eat.

- Skim milk powder adds protein — try adding two tablespoons of dry skim milk powder to the regular amount of milk in recipes.

- Use fortified milk for cooking and drinking (see recipe for fortified milk in recipe section).

- Add milk powder to hot or cold cereals, scrambled eggs, soups, gravies, to ground meat (for meat patties, meat balls, and meatloaf) casserole dishes, desserts and in baking.

- Use milk or half and half instead of water when making soup, cereals, instant cocoa, puddings and canned soups. Soy formulas may also be used.

- Add diced or ground meat to soups and to casseroles.

- Add grated cheese or chunks of cheese to sauces, vegetables, soups and casseroles.

- Add cream cheese or peanut butter to butter on hot bread.

- Add cooked cubed shrimp, canned tuna, crab meat, diced ham or sliced boiled eggs to sauces and serve over rice, cooked noodles, butter toast or hot biscuits.

- Choose dessert recipes which contain eggs such as sponge and angel food cake, egg custard, bread pudding or rice pudding.

- Add peanut butter to sauces, use on crackers, waffles or celery sticks.

- Use the recipes in the back of the book. Many have a higher than usual amount of protein.

Hints For Adding Calories To The Diet

Here are ways to add calories to the diet:

- A teaspoon of butter or margarine will add 45 calories. Mix it into hot foods such as soups, vegetables, mashed potatoes, cooked cereal and rice. Serve hot bread, more butter is used when it melts into it.

- Mayonnaise has 100 calories per tablespoon — almost twice as much as salad dressing. Use it in salads, in eggs, with lettuce on sandwiches.

- Use peanut butter (which has protein as well as calories — one tablespoon is 90 calories). Spread it on fruit such as an apple, banana, or pear, or stuff celery with it. Add it to a sandwich with mayonnaise or cream cheese.

- Spread honey on your toast, use it as a sweetner in your coffee or tea, add it to your cereal in the morning.

- Sour cream or yogurt can be used on vegetables such as potatoes, beans, carrots, squash. Try them in gravies or as a salad dressing for fruit.

- Use sour cream as a dip for fresh vegetables. For a good dessert, scoop it on fresh fruit, add brown sugar and let it sit in the refrigerator for a while. One tablespoon of sour cream is 70 calories.

Whipping cream is about 60 calories a tablespoon. Add it to pies, fruit, puddings, hot chocolate, jello and other desserts.

Add marshmallows to fruit or hot chocolate.

Have snacks ready to eat. Nuts, dried fruits, candy, popcorn, crackers and cheese, granola, ice cream, and popsicles all make good snacks. Milk shakes add calories and are especially easy to make with a blender.

Powdered coffee creamers add calories without volume — add them to gravy, soup, milk shakes, and hot cereals.

Meat, chicken and fish that are breaded are higher in calories than when broiled or roasted plain.

Add raisins, dates or chopped nuts and brown sugar to hot cereals or to cold cereals for a snack.

Look at the recipes in the back of the book — most were developed to give more than the usual number of calories.

Are You Looking For Foods Which Are Low In Fat?

Here are some foods to choose from:

- Low fat yogurt, low fat cottage cheese, 1% buttermilk, 1% low fat milk.

- Hot and cold cereals (except granola types).

- Toast with jelly or honey (no butter).

- Broth type soups.

- Crab, white fish, shrimp, light tuna (packed in water).

- Spaghetti with plain sauces.

- Veal, chicken and turkey breast and lean cuts of other meats — braise, roast or cook them without added fats. Look in the recipe section for those noted as "acceptable" under low-fat content or prepare them using the substitutes noted.

- Vegetables and vegetable juices.

- Fruits and fruit juices.

- Sauces, junket, pudding or shakes made with skim milk.

- Danish pudding and fruit pie fillings.

- Angel food cake.

- Popsicles, sherbet, gelatin ices.

- Pretzels, soda crackers, plain breads.

- Hard and jelly candies.

Are You Looking For Foods Which Are Low In Fiber?

Choose from food you normally use. Do not use foods which cause you discomfort or produce allergic reactions. Make sure you read the section titled *Problems With Diarrhea, Constipation, Bloating and Heartburn* for foods you should avoid if you have diarrhea.

Meat, fish and poultry:
Use tender cuts and ground meat. Prepare them without frying. Use mild seasoning. Suggestions: stews, roasts, meatloafs, casseroles, sandwiches and soups.

Eggs:
Use only cooked eggs. Suggestions: scrambled, poached, boiled, omelets, creamed, souffles, custard, puddings and casseroles.

Milk and cheese:
Use milk and mild cheeses if you can tolerate them (read the section titled *What Is Lactose Intolerance*). Commercial nutritional supplements and formulas are listed in the section titled *Nutritional Formulas.* Suggestions: yogurt, frozen desserts, pudding, cream sauce, soups, casseroles. Use in baking bread and making desserts.

Bread, cereals and grains:
Any product but those containing cracked grain, bran, nuts or seeds can be used. Suggestions: toast, pretzels, plain cereal and crackers, all types of breads. Grain should be well-cooked. Include in casseroles, dumplings, souffles, cheese strata, kugels and pudding.

Vegetables and potatoes:
Use only well-cooked vegetables and potatoes, removing seeds and tough skins. Vegetables which may cause discomfort are listed in the section titled *Problems With Diarrhea, Constipation, Bloating and Heartburn.* Suggestions: in cream sauces, soups, souffles, kugels and casseroles.

Fruit:
Canned or cooked fruits without seeds or tough skins and well-ripened bananas. Suggestions: in gelatins, milk shakes, frozen desserts, pudding, bread, cakes and sauces.

Other foods:
Margarine, butter, cream and oils may be used in moderation. Sugar, hard candy and syrup may be used as desired.

Are You Looking For Soft Foods Or Liquid Meals?

When preparing liquid or blended meals:

- Choose foods you normally use from those listed.
- Don't use foods which cause discomfort or produce allergic reactions for you.
- Warm meats, vegetables or potatoes before blending.
- Cut meat finely. Blend with liquids such as broth or gravy.
- Strain liquid meals if you want to avoid particles.
- Include pancakes, pudding, gelatin, custard and similar foods which can be served without blending.

If you need tube or gastrostomy feeding, ask for a consultation with the nutritionist or dietitian at the hospital to determine the contents, method of preparation and feeding techniques.

Meat, fish and poultry:
Choose tender cuts and ground meat. Use moist heat cookery such as braising, simmering and poaching. Suggestions: pot roast, stew, meatloaf, chopped liver or meat salads, casseroles, hash, soups and chowders.

Eggs:
Use only cooked eggs. Suggestions: omelets, scrambled, poached, soft boiled, eggnog (see recipe in back of book), french toast, creamed eggs, egg salad, souffles, custard and puddings, crepes or pancakes and casseroles.

Milk and cheese:
Use them as beverages and in cooking. Suggestions: fortified milk (see recipe section), yogurt, milk shakes, ice cream, frozen yogurt, pudding, cream sauce, soups, casseroles, desserts, and in baking bread.

Bread, cereals and grains:
Choose soft breads, hot or soaked cereals and cooked grains such as rice and macaroni. Bran and cracked grain products may be irritating. Suggestions: cheese strata, casseroles, kugels and puddings. Bread, biscuits and muffins may be soaked in milk coffee or soup or served with gravy and sauces.

Vegetables and potatoes:
Use cooked vegetables, removing seeds and tough skins. Tomato may be irritating. Suggestions: creamed, in omelets, soups, souffles, kugels, and casseroles.

Fruit:
Choose those which are well ripened, canned or cooked. Remove seeds and tough skins. Citrus or tart fruits may be irritating. Suggestions: gelatins, milk shakes, frozen desserts, pudding, breads, cakes and sauces.

Other Foods:
Include margarine, butter, cream, oils and sugars in foods. (see *Hints for Adding Calories To Your Diet*).

What Do You Mean By "Eating Well"?

Eating well means using a variety of foods that will give you the vitamins, minerals, protein and other elements necessary to keep the body working normally. It means having a diet that is high enough in calories to keep up your weight. It means eating foods which are high in protein because protein is needed to build and repair the skin, hair, muscles and organs in your body. People who have had surgery or illness need extra protein and other nutrients for repair of body tissues. Protein can only be used by the body for repair if you are also eating enough calories. If you do not eat enough calories the body will use the protein in your body for energy instead of for repair.

A good rule to follow is to try to eat a mixed diet without omitting any of the basic four groups of foods for any period of time:

Fruit and vegetable group:
Four servings a day of salads, cooked vegetable, raw or cooked fruits and juices supply some of the vital vitamins and minerals your body needs. A serving can be one half cup of cooked vegetables, fruit or juice or one cup or one piece of raw fruit or vegetable.

Meat group:
Three servings a day of meats, fish, poultry, eggs, cheese give you proteins as well as many vitamins and minerals. A serving is two ounces of meat, fish, or poultry, or two eggs or two ounces of cheese or one cup of dried beans, peas or nuts, or four tablespoons of peanut butter.

Grain group:
Four servings a day of grains and cereals supply a variety of vitamins, minerals and some protein. A serving is one slice of bread or one cup of cereal or one half cup of pasta, rice or grits.

Milk group:
Two servings each day of milk or other dairy products give you protein, a variety of vitamins and the best source of calcium. These supply similar amounts of calcium: One serving is one cup of milk or yogurt, one and a half ounces of cheese, one cup pudding, one and three quarters cup of ice cream or two cups of cottage cheese.

What Is Lactose Intolerance?

If you have lactose intolerance it means you have problems digesting or absorbing the milk sugar called lactose. This is often an inherited trait, but the symptoms may occur after treatment with some antibiotics, with abdominal radiation or any treatment that affects the g.i. tract. The part of your intestines which breaks down lactose is not working properly. For some, the symptoms (gas, cramping, diarrhea) disappear a few weeks or months after the treatments are finished or when the intestine is healed. For others, a permanent change in eating habits is in order.

In general, cancer patients with this particular problem will be advised by their doctors to follow a diet that is low in foods which contain lactose. Lactose is chiefly found in milk and in many dairy products. It may be present in foods or added to them in the manufacturing process. Read the labels until you are familiar with these products. If milk had been a main source of protein in your diet, it will be important to use soybean formulas and aged cheese so that you will get enough protein and other nutrients. Look for recipes in this book that are acceptable for a low-lactose diet or tell you what to substitute to make them acceptable. (The substitutes include aged cheese, soybean formulas, milk-free kosher or diet margarine and other non-dairy products.)

Foods High In Lactose:

- Milk (liquid or dry solids), ice cream, (some people can use acidophilus milk or milk treated with Lact-aid which has less lactose than regular milk)
- All types of cheese, except natural cheese aged 90 days
- Instant coffee
- Cocoa and most chocolate beverages
- Cream (sweet and sour)
- Desserts with custard or cream filling

Foods Which Contain Smaller Amounts Of Lactose:

One would advise caution in using these foods also:

- Breads, cereals, crackers and breakfast items containing milk, butter, margarine, dry milk solids or whey
- Powdered coffee cream
- Cold cuts or frankfurters containing dry milk solids
- Meats that are creamed or breaded
- Liver, liver sausage, sweetbreads, brain
- Gravy made with milk, cream, butter or margarine
- Cream sauces and cream soups, dried soups
- Party dips
- Butter or margarine with dry milk solids
- Salad dressings with dairy products added

- Any vegetables seasoned with margarine, butter or cream sauce
- Canned or frozen vegetables prepared with lactose (most canned vegetables do **not** contain lactose)
- Commercial french fried potatoes, instant potatoes, mashed potatoes
- Spice blends, monosodium glutamate extender (pure monosodium glutamate is lactose-free)
- Cakes, cookies or pastries made with milk, butter, margarine or whey
- Desserts with commercial fruit fillings
- Yogurt (some people can eat it without a problem)
- Sherbet
- Fruit cake blends
- Butterscotch, carmels, chocolate candy, molasses, peppermints, toffee
- Cordials and liqueurs, maraschino cherries
- Powdered soft drinks
- Dietetic and diabetic preparations (check labels)

Note: Kosher products marked "Pareve" are milk-free.

Look for recipes in this booklet marked "lactose free" or "acceptable" under low-lactose or prepare them using the substitute noted.

How To Save Time And Energy

One of the people we talked with told us she really didn't have any "problems" with eating during her chemotherapy treatment — she was just too tired to cook. We heard this often. Time and energy need to be saved by both the patient and family members. It is important for cancer patients to realize their bodies need both rest and nourishment during and after surgery, radiation, chemotherapy or immunotherapy cycles.

Try To Save Time In Preparing Meals

Meal preparation can be difficult when a family member is ill, and the "cook" must also attend to nursing tasks and perhaps prepare special foods for the patient. When the cook is also the patient, mealtimes can become a source of frustration. Solutions depend upon your needs and the available help. Try some of these suggestions:

- Let someone else do the cooking.

- If you know that your recovery time from treatment or surgery is going to be longer than one or two days, prepare a helper list. Decide who can help you shop, cook, set the table and clean up. Write it down, discuss it and post it where it can be easily seen. If there are children involved, plan a small reward.

- Write out menus, choosing things which you or your family can put together easily. Casseroles, t.v. dinners, hotdogs, hamburgers, meals which you have prepared and frozen ahead are all good solutions. Make larger batches when you cook to be frozen so you will have them for future use. Add instructions so that other people can help you.

- Use shopping lists. Keep them handy so that they can be used as guides either by yourself or other people in the future.

- When making casseroles for freezing, only partially cook the rice and macaroni products. They will cook further in the reheating process. Add 1/2 cup liquid to refrigerated or frozen casseroles when reheating since they absorb moisture during refrigeration. Remember that frozen casseroles take a long time to heat completely — at least 45 minutes in deep dishes.

- Accept gifts of food and offers of help from family and friends. If you can't use the food right away, freeze it. That homecooked meal can break the monotony of quickie suppers and can save lots of time when there is a tight schedule. Remember to date the food when you put it in the refrigerator or freezer and use it before it can get spoiled.

- Have as few dishes, pots and pans to wash as possible. Cook in dishes and pans which can also be used as attractive servers. Use paper napkins, disposable dishes, especially for dessert. Paper cups are fine for the kids and for medicines. Disposable pans are a great timesaver during a period of overwork — foil containers from frozen foods make good disposable pans. Soak dirty dishes to cut down washing time.

- When special foods must be prepared such as soft dishes or dinners in the blender or food processor, choose foods which the family can also eat. Set aside enough food to be blended for the patient, then serve the rest of the family. Cook soft foods everyone can eat, such as omelets, scrambled eggs, macaroni and cheese, meatloaf or tuna salad sandwiches. Serve plain rice or noodles to the patient if needed and add a sauce for the rest of the family.

- Use mixes, frozen ready-to-eat main dishes, and take-out foods whenever possible. This is especially important for those who are quite tired. The less time spent cooking and cleaning up, the more time for relaxation and the family.

- Keep snacks handy. Small meals often may keep calories and nutrition up, even if you are not eating as much as usual at one sitting.

- If you are cooking for a sick person, try not to get upset if the person doesn't feel like eating. Understand that there will be days like that. Look over the suggestions in this booklet for adding protein and calories so that the foods offered are nourishing. Ask the patient what he wants to eat. Offer small portions.

Helpful Appliances

It is not necessary to equip your kitchen with expensive appliances, but you may decide to purchase a piece which will be useful over a period of time. The persons we talked with found several of the small appliances very useful. (If you need a blender for a short period of time, you may be able to borrow one from the loan closet of your local American Cancer Society Unit.)

Before you buy any appliance ask yourself these questions:

- Is it easy to operate? Are the directions clearly written?
- Is it light enough to pick up? Does it move about easily?
- Will it fit on the countertop, table or floorspace without being in the way?
- Will it save enough time and energy to be worthwhile?

Blender:
Very important and useful for soft and liquid food preparation. A simple inexpensive model with three speeds is good enough to mix, blend or make liquid most foods. Easy to use and clean and takes little counter space.

Electric frying pan:
Versatile, helpful time and energy saver. It simplifies meal preparation for the single person or small family. Can warm, fry, simmer and bake. Some newer models even have a broiler in the lid. Usually lightweight, it takes up little space and is easy to clean.

Steamer:
Inexpensive. Fits into existing pot. Does not overcook food. Makes food more attractive without loss of minerals and vitamins.

Pressure cooker:

Can be used to steam, soften or tenderize any amount of food in a short period of time. Somewhat noisy. Use a timer to insure proper cooking for there is a tendency to overcook. Takes practice to operate correctly. Heavy but cleans easily.

Toaster-broiler oven:

Valuable for any size family, as it warms, toasts, broils, and bakes. Comes in many different models and sizes. Requires some counterspace, is lightweight and relatively easy to clean.

Electric crockpot:

Makes soft, simmered food. Useful for "no fuss" soup, stews and similar cooking. Look for one that handles and cleans easily.

Food processor:

It can chop, slice, shred, blend, and puree foods as well as mix batters for baking. Takes some practice to operate correctly, but it is easily cleaned and stored. Can be an expensive appliance, depending on manufacturer.

Microwave oven:

Expensive. Time and energy saver as defrosting and cooking time is much faster. Paper, plastic or glassware can be used for cooking and eating. Cleaning is minimal.

Dishwasher:

Expensive but great energy sa` for everyone, even the single p son. Smaller machine with on or two cycles is adequate.

Recipes

The recipes were especially chosen to help solve the problems discussed in the book. In order to be included the recipes also had to be high in nutritional value, easy to make, good tasting and useable for the family as well as for the patient. You will find some old favorites — but calories, protein, or other nutrients have been added. All of them have been taste-tested and only the favorites from the taste-testing have been included.

The recipes used are marked either acceptable or not acceptable in each of four categories or substitutes are noted to make them acceptable.

Low fat: Recipes which contain less than 10 grams of fat per serving (for meat or main entrees) or 5 grams or less for other kinds of foods are designated as acceptable in the low fat category. An occasional recipe is marked fat free — that means there is no significant fat content.

Low lactose: Foods containing minimal amounts of lactose are designated as acceptable in the low-lactose category. An occasional recipe is noted as lactose-free, which means it contains no lactose. You will notice that many of the recipes noted as low lactose use non-dairy creamers or soy formulas (usually sold as infant soy formulas in the supermarkets).

Non-dairy creamers contribute flavor and calories, mostly from fats and oils. Much has been done recently to improve the taste of soy formulas which are now a slightly yeasty flavor. They have nutritional content similar to milk, containing valuable protein, vitamins and minerals.

Low sodium: Recipes which are suitable for the American Heart Association Mild Sodium Restriction (2400-4500 mg.) are listed as acceptable under the category low sodium. In many cases directions are given to modify the regular recipes.

Sugar free: For the convenience of diabetics, recipes which are sugar free or low in concentrated carbohydrates are listed as acceptable under the category sugar free.

Abbreviations: In all recipes, tsp. is teaspoon, Tbl. is tablespoon and lb. is pound.

NOTE: No product endorsement (brand name listing) is intended in this book. Brands are named only to insure specific ingredient content, or when a particular brand was consistently acceptable in taste testing results. Similar products in your own area may work as well, with little or no change needed in the recipe.

Soft, moist and nourishing, just as popular with or without milk.

Macaroni and Cheese

1 cup milk
1 Tbl. flour
1 - 2 Tbls. margarine
1 tsp. minced onion

salt and pepper to taste
1 tsp. dry mustard (optional)
2 cups elbow macaroni,
   cooked and drained
1 cup shredded cheddar cheese

Measure milk into the pan and blend in flour until no lumps remain. Add margarine, onion and other seasonings and cook until sauce thickens. Stir in macaroni and cheese. Bake in greased one quart casserole, uncovered, at 400° for 15 minutes, or until slightly browned and bubbly. May be frozen before baking. Serves four.

Low fat:	Not acceptable
Low lactose:	Substitute formula for milk; use non-dairy margarine and aged cheddar cheese.
Low sodium:	Omit salt
Sugar free:	Acceptable
Calories:	275 per serving
Protein:	11 gms. per serving

Cheesy Hamburger Casserole

1 cup macaroni, uncooked
½ lb. ground meat (beef, veal)
½ small onion, chopped

¾ cup tomato sauce or
  chopped tomatoes
½ can (10 ounces) cheddar
  cheese soup

Cook macaroni until slightly tender. Drain, set aside. Brown ground meat and onions in small skillet. Add tomatoes and simmer 10 minutes. Oil a one quart casserole, and spoon in ⅓ of meat mixture. Add cooked macaroni, then the remainder of meat mixture. Spread cheese soup overall (may be frozen, un-baked). Cover the casserole tightly, and bake at 400° until bub-bly. Makes four servings.

Low fat: Not acceptable

Low lactose: Omit cheese soup, add ½ cup water and 2 ozs.
                 aged cheddar cheese.

Low sodium: Substitute 2 ozs. cheddar cheese for soup.

Sugar free: Acceptable

Calories: 215 per serving

Protein: 16 gms. per serving

This is a simple one dish meal, a cousin to Quiche Lorraine. Just the thing for a night when you don't want to fuss.

Cheese-Spinach Pie

⅓ cup chopped onion
1 Tbl. margarine
¼ lb. sliced cheese (swiss or meunster)
1 cup cooked, chopped spinach (drained)

3 large eggs
⅓ - ½ cup of milk
½ tsp. salt
dash pepper
9-inch pie shell or thin biscuit dough to fit a 9-inch pie pan

Cook onion in margarine until tender; cool. Lay slices of cheese over pie dough, follow with spinach, then onions. Beat eggs, adding enough milk to make one cup. Add seasonings and pour over ingredients in the pie shell. Bake in 400° oven about 35 minutes, or until a knife comes out clean. Serve piping hot. (Can be frozen after baking.) Serves four.

Variation: Substitute cooked, chopped broccoli, green beans, zucchini or peas for spinach.

Low fat:	Not acceptable
Low lactose:	Substitute soy formula for milk. Use non-dairy margarine and aged natural cheese and milk free dough.
Low sodium:	Not acceptable
Sugar free:	Acceptable
Calories:	454 per serving (pie crust); 353 per serving (biscuit)
Protein:	18 gms. per serving

A reliable, mildly flavored recipe which can adapt to your needs.

Basic Meatloaf or Meatballs

2 Tbls. dry bread or cracker
  crumbs
1 Tbl. water
½ lb. ground beef or veal
1 egg

¼ tsp. minced onion
salt and pepper to taste
1 Tbl. oil or margarine
2 slices onion

Combine crumbs and water in small mixing bowl. Add meat, minced onion, egg and seasonings. Mix until well blended. Form into patties one inch, meatballs or a loaf. Brown in oil or margarine in skillet, turn to brown both sides. Add sliced onion, lower heat, cover and simmer for at least 15 minutes, 30 minutes for meatloaf. You can also bake at 350°. For meatballs bake 30 minutes, turning after 15 minutes. For meatloaf bake one hour. Can be frozen raw or cooked. Makes four servings.

Low fat: Acceptable

Low lactose: Use milk-free bread crumbs.

Low sodium: Omit salt

Sugar free: Acceptable

Calories: 125 per serving

Protein: 13 gms. per serving

Favorite of young and old, it's easy to eat.

Sloppy Joes

½ lb. ground meat   ½ cup quick barbecue sauce
1 small onion, diced   1 Tbl. raw oatmeal

Brown meat and onion in small skillet. Add barbecue sauce, oatmeal and enough water to cover meat. Heat to boiling, turn
down heat to simmer, cover pan and cook 15 minutes or until
thickened and meat is soft. Serve on buns, toast, or hard rolls.
Can be frozen after cooking. Serves four.

Low fat: Acceptable

Low lactose: Acceptable

Low sodium: Not acceptable

Sugar free: Not acceptable

Calories: 160 per serving

Protein: 12 gms. per serving

These are tender meatballs with gourmet flavor.

Swedish Meatballs

1 lb. ground round steak   ⅔ tsp. salt
½ cup plain bread crumbs   dash pepper and allspice
1 egg, slightly beaten   1 Tbl. margarine

Mix all ingredients except margarine with a fork until well
blended. Form into balls, brown in margarine in medium sized
skillet. Remove meatballs from pan. Make a thickened gravy
with the drippings. Return meatballs to gravy and simmer,
covered, for 1 to 1½ hours. May be frozen raw or cooked.
Serves four.

Contributed by D. Ruth Gilbert

Low fat: Not acceptable

Lactose free: Use milk-free bread crumbs.

Low sodium: Omit salt

Sugar free: Acceptable

Calories: 281 per serving

Protein: 25 gms. per serving

Supremely simple to make, this is a delightfully seasoned entree.

Chicken Supreme

1 can (10 ozs.) cream of
   mushroom soup
½ cup orange juice
½ cup water

1 cup rice, uncooked
6 pieces chicken
¼ envelope onion soup mix

Combine first four ingredients and pour into greased two-quart casserole. Lay chicken on top. Sprinkle with dry onion soup mix. Cover casserole, airtight, with heavy aluminum foil. Bake two hours without opening the foil, at 350°. Can be frozen after baking. Serves six.

Contributed by a patient

Low fat:	Remove excess skin from chicken.
Low lactose:	Acceptable
Low sodium:	Not acceptable
Sugar free:	Acceptable
Calories:	295 per serving
Protein:	18 gms. per serving

Tender and lightly seasoned, this simple meal can be a complete meal with rice, noodles or mashed potatoes.

Chicken Skillet Supper

2 – 3 lbs. frying chicken, cut up   1 can water
½ can (10 oz.) vegetarian-   2 sprigs of parsley
   vegetable soup   1 basil leaf (optional)

Place chicken, skin side down in cold skillet. Brown over medium heat, turning to brown inside. Remove from heat (chicken skin can easily be removed at this point if you wish). Pour off all fat remaining in skillet. Replace chicken, pour soup and water over chicken and add seasonings. Simmer one hour in covered skillet turning pieces once to keep them moist. May be frozen after cooking. Serves four.

Tomato special: Substitute ½ can of cream of tomato for vegetarian-vegetable soup. Add 1 package (10 oz.) of mixed frozen vegetables with the soup and water.

Creamy chicken: Substitute ½ can of cream of chicken for vegetarian-vegetable soup, add 1 package (10 oz.) frozen peas and carrots.

Low fat: Remove skin if needed.

Low lactose: Acceptable

Low sodium: Not acceptable

Sugar free: Acceptable

Calories: 200 per serving

Protein: 24 gms. per serving

This mild flavored tuna dish is complemented with a tossed salad.

Robert's Tuna Bake

1 can (7 ozs.) water packed tuna, broken in small pieces
1 can (10 ozs.) tomato soup
½ cup milk
¼ lb. American or cheddar cheese
1 lb. box of elbow macaroni, cooked

Mix first four ingredients in saucepan and heat until cheese melts. Add macaroni to sauce and mix well. Pour into greased baking dish and bake at 350° for 20 minutes. Serves eight.

Chicken Noodle Bake: Substitute cream of celery soup for tomato, 1 cup diced chicken for tuna, cooked noodles for elbow macaroni.

Egg Noodle Bake: Substitute cream of chicken soup for tomato, 3 or more hard boiled eggs, sliced, for tuna, and cooked noodles for elbow macaroni.

Contributed by Mr. Robert L. Card

Low fat:	Acceptable
Low lactose:	Substitute soy formula for milk. Used aged cheddar cheese.
Low sodium:	Not acceptable
Sugar free:	Acceptable
Calories:	435 per serving (tuna bake)
Protein:	24 gms. per serving (tuna bake)

A surprising balance of flavors will please busy cooks and their families.

Tuna Broccoli Casserole

2 packages (10 ozs.) frozen broccoli, whole or chopped
2 cans (7 ozs.) water packed tuna, broken in small pieces
1 can (10 ozs.) cream of mushroom soup diluted with ½ cup of
  milk
1 cup grated cheddar or American cheese
½ cup plain bread crumbs
2 Tbls. melted margarine

Cook broccoli according to package directions, drain and place
in shallow two-quart casserole. Add tuna and cover with diluted
mushroom soup. Sprinkle with cheese. Add bread crumbs to
melted butter and sprinkle over casserole. Bake at 350° for 20
minutes. Serves 5.

Contributed by a patient

Low fat: Not acceptable

Low lactose: Substitute aged cheddar cheese, non-dairy
                margarine and use water instead of milk.

Low sodium: Not acceptable

Sugar free: Acceptable

Calories: 290 per serving

Protein: 25 gms. per serving

A light potato salad, mildly seasoned for the sensitive palate.

Creamy Potato Salad

⅓ cup plain low fat yogurt
⅓ cup mayonnaise
¼ tsp. finely minced or scraped
  onion
1 sprig of parsley, chopped fine

¼ cup chopped celery or green
  pepper (optional)
2 potatoes, boiled and diced
2 hard boiled eggs, diced
salt to taste

Blend yogurt, mayonnaise, onion, parsley, celery and pepper. Stir in remaining ingredients. Cover and refrigerate for several hours. Serves four.

Ricotta Potato Salad: Add ⅓ cup ricotta cheese to mayonnaise.

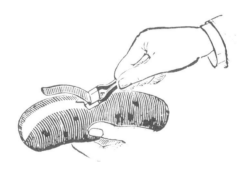

Low fat:	Not acceptable
Low lactose:	Use yogurt made only from cultured pasteurized milk.
Low sodium:	Omit salt
Sugar free:	Acceptable
Calories:	245 per serving
Protein:	5 gms per serving

These pancakes have double the protein of regular pancakes. Two of them equal one ounce of meat in protein content.

High Protein Pancakes

½ cup milk

2 Tbls. dry milk

1 egg (2 for a thinner crepe-type)

2 tsps. of oil

½ – ¾ cups pancake mix

Measure milk, dry milk, egg and oil into blender or bowl. Beat until egg is well blended. Add pancake mix. Stir or blend at low speed until mix is wet but some lumps remain. Cook on hot greased griddle or fry pan, turning when firm to brown the other side. These can be kept warm in a warm oven, or in a covered pan on low heat. Makes seven 4" pancakes.

Note: If there is batter left over, it will keep one day in the refrigerator, or it can be made into pancakes, cooled and wrapped in foil to be frozen for later use. To reheat, leave in foil and place in 450° oven for 15 minutes. If using a toaster-oven, unwrap them, brush with margarine and toast as for light toast.

Low fat: Acceptable

Low lactose: Not acceptable

Low sodium: Acceptable

Sugar free: Acceptable

Calories: 77 per pancake

Protein: 3 gms. per pancake

These pancakes have the high protein quality without a drop of milk.

Low Lactose Pancakes

1 egg (2 for crepe-type)
½ cup soy formula

2 tsps. milk-free margarine,
  melted
½ cup milk-free pancake mix*

Into bowl or blender put egg, soy formula and melted margarine. Beat to blend. Stir in mix until wet, but some lumps remain. Cook on greased or oiled pan (use only milk-free margarine, bacon fat or shortening) until firm enough to turn over. Brown other side. Keep warm in oven or in covered pan on low heat. If you wish to freeze pancakes, follow directions in recipe for High Protein Pancakes. Makes six 4"pancakes.

Low fat: Use teflon coated pan.

Low lactose: Acceptable

Low sodium: Acceptable

Sugar free: Acceptable

Calories: 88 per pancake

Protein: 2 gms. per pancake

*Pillsbury's Hungry Jack Extra Lights is a lactose-free mix. Aunt Jemima's Whole Wheat may contain a small amount of lactose.

Quick Barbecue Sauce

½ cup catsup
2 tsps. salad style mustard
½ tsp. lemon juice

1 Tbl. brown sugar
½ tsp. onion salt

Mix together in small saucepan. Heat until boiling, stirring as it cooks.

Serving suggestions: Make sloppy Joes. Use as a barbecue sauce for hot dogs, chicken or meatballs. (It will easily coat eight pieces of chicken.) Use as a marinade for chicken or meat: pour over pieces in a deep dish, and refrigerate in marinade, at least 12 hours to tenderize. Makes ½ cup.

Low fat:	Acceptable
Low lactose:	Acceptable
Low sodium:	Not acceptable
Sugar free:	Not acceptable
Calories:	208 per recipe
Protein:	2 gms. per recipe

A quick, flavorful sauce everybody enjoys on eggs or meat.

Creole Sauce

½ small onion, sliced
1 or 2 frying peppers (1 bell
    pepper) cleaned and sliced
2 Tbls. oil
2 cups chopped fresh tomatoes
    or 15 ounce can of tomatoes

½ tsp. salt
2 Tbls. sugar
1 tsp. vinegar
1 Tbls. cornstarch
water

Fry onion and peppers in oil until onion is clean and pepper is
spotted with brown. Add tomatoes, salt, sugar and vinegar.
Bring to boiling, turn down to simmer. Cover and cook at least 20
minutes to blend the flavors. Thicken just before serving with
cornstarch dissolved in a little water. Use on eggs or meat.
Makes 2 cups.

Low fat: Use only 1 Tbl. oil.

Lactose free

Low sodium: Omit salt

Sugar free: Omit sugar

Calories: 598 per recipe; 150 per serving

Protein: 2 gms. per serving

An unexpected favorite. This tangy sauce is often used on meat or chicken by those interviewed.

Sweet and Sour Sauce

¼ cup vinegar
1 cup catsup
1 Tbl. soy sauce
½ red or green pepper, cubed
½ cup honey or brown sugar
  (packed)

½ tsp. salt
1 can (8 ounce size) pineapple
  chunks (optional)
Water
2 Tbls. cornstarch

Mix all ingredients except cornstarch in saucepan. Bring to boil. Turn heat down to simmer, stirring occasionally and cook for at least 20 minutes to allow flavors to blend. Dissolve cornstarch in small amount of water. Add, stirring until thickened. (You can omit cornstarch and allow the sauce to thicken by cooking it longer). Use on meat or chicken. Makes 2 cups.

Fat free

Low lactose: Acceptable

Low sodium: Not acceptable

Sugar free: Not acceptable

Calories: 590 per cup

Protein: 3 gms. per cup

The sweet-tart taste of this sauce is a change from sweet syrup. Good on pancakes and waffles.

Fresh Peach Sauce

1 large peach, peeled and thinly sliced
1½ Tbls. sugar

¼ cup water
1 tsp. cornstarch
dash nutmeg

Combine ingredients in a small pan, stir until cornstarch is dissolved. Cook over medium heat until sauce boils and is thickened. Serves one.

Fat free

Lactose free

Low sodium: Acceptable

Sugar free: Substitute sugar substitute.

Calories: 140 per recipe

Protein: 0

This tasty sauce is good for many toppings.

Milk-Free Butterscotch Sauce

⅓ cup brown sugar, packed
2 tsp. cornstarch
¼ cup non-dairy creamer

¼ cup water
1 Tbl. honey
1 Tbl. milk-free margarine
½ tsp. vanilla

Mix brown sugar and cornstarch in small saucepan. Slowly add non-dairy creamer and water, stirring until cornstarch dissolves. Add honey and margarine. Cook over medium heat, stirring constantly, until sauce is thickened and comes to a boil. Remove from heat. Add vanilla. Cool and store in a covered container in refrigerator. Makes about ½ cup.

Milk-Free Chocolate: Stir in one heaping Tbl. cocoa with cornstarch. If too thick, add a little water after it comes to a boil.

Low fat:	Omit margarine.
Lactose free	
Low sodium:	Acceptable
Sugar free:	Not acceptable
Calories:	599 per recipe, 85 per Tbl.
Protein:	0

Doubles the protein in each cup of milk. Used in many recipes in this booklet.

Fortified Milk

1 quart milk, homogenized or   1 cup instant non-fat dry milk
   1% low fat

Pour liquid milk into deep bowl. Add dry milk and beat slowly
with beater until dry milk is dissolved (usually less than 5 minutes). Refrigerate. The flavor improves after several hours.
Makes one quart.

Low fat:	Acceptable
Low lactose:	Not acceptable
Low sodium:	Acceptable
Sugar free:	Acceptable (use as two low-fat milk exchanges)
Calories:	275 per cup with homogenized milk 195 per cup with low-fat milk
Protein:	19 gms. per cup

Egg-Nogs

Egg-nogs are usually a popular food — but they can also be a
source of trouble. The age old recipe for making egg-nog was to
break a raw egg into a cup of milk, add sugar and vanilla and whip
it together. The trouble begins after you've eaten it – somewhere
further along in your system. Raw egg whites contain an anti-
vitamin (avidin) which interferes with the absorption of biotin, an
essential nutrient. A second, but no less important fact, is that raw
eggs can be carriers of the salmonella organisms which produce
diarrhea and a host of other miseries.

What to do? Try a cooked egg product such as soft custard, baked custard or pudding with eggs. Another method of producing a safe egg-nog — since there are no salmonella-free egg-nog mixes on the market, is to try this Blender Egg-Nog.

Blender Egg-Nog

1 cup cold fortified milk	1 tsp. vanilla (generous)
1½ Tbls. sugar	1 fresh egg (make sure it has no cracks in the shell)

Put milk, sugar and vanilla into blender. In small pan heat two inches of water to boiling. Rinse egg in warm running water for a few seconds and break egg into water. Cook for two to three minutes over medium heat until white is firm (do not boil since boiling tends to harden egg). Scoop egg out of water and place directly into blender. Blend at high speed, covered, for about 15 seconds or until egg is well blended. Strain to take out any tiny particles. (Do not sniff egg-nog when you finish blending it: it will have the sulfur smell of a hot cooked egg for a few seconds.)

You can serve the egg-nog immediately for it is room temperature: most of the people who tasted it liked it best at this temperature. You can make it in larger batches and store it in the refrigerator or freezer. Try it with nutmeg, ice cream or brandy (if doctor allows). Makes one serving.

Low fat:	Substitute low fat fortified milk.
Low lactose:	Substitute non-dairy creamer or soy formula for milk.
Low sodium:	Acceptable
Sugar free:	Substitute sugar substitute.
Calories:	423 (314 with soy formula) per recipe
Protein:	26 gms. (12 gms. with soy formula) per recipe

A tasty banana shake is a rich potassium source.

Vera's Banana Milkshake

1 whole ripe banana, sliced   vanilla (few drops)
1 cup milk

Measure into blender and blend at high speed until smooth.
Serves one.

Banana-butterscotch: Add 2 Tbls. of butterscotch sauce with
banana.

Contributed by Vera Bagley

Low fat:	Use low fat milk
Low lactose:	Substitute soy formula for milk.
Low sodium:	Acceptable
Sugar free:	Acceptable
Calories:	275 per recipe
Protein:	9 gms. per recipe

The flavor of fresh strawberries, but from the freezer.

Pearl's Strawberry Milkshake

1/2 cup frozen strawberries
1 scoop ice cream
1/2 cup milk

Mix or blend until smooth. Serves one.

contributed by Pearl L. Howard

Low fat:	Use low fat milk and ice milk
Low lactose:	Not acceptable
Low sodium:	Acceptable
Sugar free:	Substitute unsweetened strawberries. Diabetics on measured diets must make needed adjustments in their diets.
Calories:	355 per recipe
Protein:	7 gms. per recipe

Favorite milkshake flavors with extra protein.

High Protein Milkshakes

1 cup fortified milk
1 generous scoop ice cream
½ tsp. vanilla

2 Tbls. of butterscotch,
   chocolate or your favorite
   fruit syrup or sauce

Measure all ingredients into blender. Blend at low speed about 10 seconds. Make one serving.

Low fat:	Use low fat fortified milk and ice milk.
Low lactose:	Not acceptable
Low sodium:	Acceptable
Sugar free:	Not acceptable
Calories:	485 per serving
Protein:	22 gms. per serving

Imitation milkshakes for people who cannot drink milk or eat ice cream. Enjoy! Enjoy!

Citrus Fake Shakes

1 frozen citrus fruit juice bar (2½ ozs.) or 2 bars (1¾ ozs.) same flavor
½ cup chilled Isomil, Neomullsoy
¼ tsp. vanilla

Remove citrus bar from freezer and allow to thaw slightly (about 5 – 10 minutes until soft). Break bar into pieces into blender. Add other ingredients and blend at low speed for 10 seconds. Makes one serving.

Double citrus: You can increase the use of orange juice without drinking it by adding 1 Tbl. frozen orange juice concentrate and 1 Tbl. sugar to the lemon or orange flavor Fake Shake before blending.

Low fat:	Not acceptable
Low lactose:	Acceptable
Low sodium:	Acceptable
Sugar free:	Not acceptable
Calories:	186 per serving
Protein:	3 gms. per serving

Other Fake Shakes

Butterscotch:

½ cup chilled or partially frozen Isomil or Neomullsoy
¼ tsp. vanilla
2 Tbls. milk-free Butterscotch sauce

Blend all at low speed about 10 seconds. Using the partially frozen liquid will produce a much colder, thicker shake. Makes one serving.

Chocolate:

Use 2 Tbls. Hershey's chocolate syrup in place of butterscotch. (Commercial chocolate syrups are often made without milk or lactose, but always read the ingredient labels.)

Butterscotch Banana:

Add ½ well ripened, sliced banana to ingredients for butter-scotch shake.

Peanut Butter-Honey:

Omit butterscotch sauce. Mix together in a cup: ¼ cup soy formula or non-dairy creamer, 2 Tbls. peanut butter, 1 Tbl. honey and ¼ tsp. vanilla. Place partially frozen liquid in blender, then add peanut butter mixture. Blend for about 10 seconds, or until smooth.

Fake Shake Sherbet:

Follow recipe for Peanut Butter-Honey above. (You can double or triple recipe easily to save time.) Pour shake into small container. Freeze two hours or until it begins to harden around edges. Scrape into bowl and mix thoroughly, until lumps disappear. Return to container and refreeze two hours or until firm.

Fake Shake Ice Cream:

Any of the shakes above can be frozen into ice creams, using the same method as for Fake Shake Sherbet.

Low fat:	Not acceptable
Lactose free	
Low sodium:	Acceptable
Sugar free:	Not acceptable
Calories:	253 per serving (Butterscotch/soy formula)
Protein:	8 gms. per serving (Butterscotch/soy formula)

An occasional drink has helped boost many a lagging appetite. For many it is part of their usual pre-dinner routine. It is important to know whether your physician allows this before you sample the enriched drinks.

Fruit Smoothie

2 Tbls. blackberry or cherry cordial ¾ cup chilled or partially frozen half and half

Mix or blend until smooth. Serve in a fancy glass frosted, if you like. Serves one.

Panamanian Smoothie:

Omit cordial, add 2 Tbls. chocolate syrup and 2 Tbls. rum.

Creme de Menthe Smoothie:

Omit cordial, add 2 Tbls. creme de menthe and 2 Tbls. vanilla ice cream (omit ice cream for low lactose).

Low fat:	Not acceptable
Low lactose:	Substitute non-dairy creamer and omit ice cream. The cordials do contain some lactose.
Low sodium:	Acceptable
Sugar free:	Not acceptable
Calories:	295 per serving (Fruit Smoothie) 400 per serving (Panamanian) 330 per serving (Creme de Menthe with ice cream)
Protein:	5 gms. per serving (Fruit Smoothie) 6 gms. per serving (Panamanian and Creme de Menthe)

Amaretto Creme

½ cup chilled half and half   1 Tbl. Amaretto cordial
2 Tbls. vanilla ice cream

Mix until smooth. Serve in stemmed glass. Serves one.

Butterscotch Brandy Creme:

Omit Amaretto, add 2 Tbls. butterscotch sauce and 1 Tbl. brandy.

Low fat: Not acceptable

Low lactose: Substitute non-dairy creamer and omit ice
                 cream (Amaretto).
              Substitute non-dairy creamer and milk free
                 butterscotch sauce (Butterscotch Brandy Creme).

Low sodium: Acceptable

Sugar free: Not acceptable

Calories: 245 per serving

Protein: 4 gms. per serving

A high protein snack of good quality — the milk protein balanced by the peanut protein.

Peanut Butter Snack Spread

1 Tbl. instant dry milk	1 Tbl. honey
1 tsp. water	3 heaping Tbls. peanut butter
1 tsp. vanilla	

Combine dry milk, water and vanilla, stirring to moisten. Add honey and peanut butter, stirring slowly until liquid begins to blend with peanut butter. Spread between graham crackers or milk lunch crackers. The spread can also be formed into balls, chilled and eaten as candy. Keeps well in refrigerator, but is difficult to spread when cold. Makes ⅓ cup.

Molasses Taffy Flavor: Substitute molasses for honey.

Low fat:	Not acceptable
Low lactose:	Substitute 1 Tbl. soy formula for milk and water.
Low sodium:	Use unsalted peanut butter.
Sugar free:	Not acceptable
Calories:	440 per recipe
Protein:	17 gms. per recipe

This natural fiber snack or cereal comes with the nutrition of milk. It can also be made without milk.

Granola I

1½ cups quick oatmeal	½ cup chopped nuts
½ cup regular wheat germ	2 Tbls. oil
½ cup coconut	⅔ cup sweetened condensed
½ tsp. salt	milk

Measure oatmeal, wheat germ, coconut, salt and nuts into mixing bowl, stirring to blend. Add oil and mix thoroughly. Pour in condensed milk and blend well. Sprinkle a handful of wheat germ on a cookie sheet and gently spread mixture on top. Bake in 325° oven, about 25 minutes. Check mix as it bakes — after the first ten minutes, mix will begin to brown. Stir it on cookie sheet every ten minutes until it is as brown as you like. Cool on pan, store in covered container in refrigerator.

Granola II: Omit milk. Add ½ cup honey. Bake as above.

Chocolate Chip: Put hot mixture in bowl. Stir in ½ cup of chocolate chips.

Raisin: Stir in 1 cup of raisins after the mixture cools.

Low fat:	Not acceptable
Low lactose:	Use only Granola II recipe.
Low sodium:	Not acceptable
Sugar free:	Not acceptable
Calories:	330 per ½ cup Granola I, 340 per ½ cup Granola II.
Protein:	9 gms. per ½ cup Granola I, 7 gms. per ½ cup Granola II.

A chewy delightful bar. Great with tea or for a snack for the children with milk.

Granola Bars

¾ cup quick cooking oatmeal   1 egg
½ cup Granola II   ¼ tsp. vanilla extract
½ cup coconut   1 Tbl. honey
½ cup brown sugar, (packed)   ¼ tsp. salt
¼ cup melted margarine   ¼ cup flour

Measure oatmeal, granola, coconut and brown sugar together in deep bowl. Mix well. Pour melted margarine over all and blend thoroughly. Beat the egg, extract, honey and salt together. Pour this over dry ingredients, stirring to blend. Add flour, stirring until smoothly mixed. Press mixture onto greased, floured 11 x 7 inch shallow baking pan or cookie sheet. Bake at 325° for 35 minutes. Cool slightly, cut into bars, and remove from the pan while warm. Makes 18 bars.

Low fat: Acceptable

Low lactose: Acceptable

Low sodium: Omit salt.

Sugar free: Not acceptable

Calories: 60

Protein: 2 gms.

Fiber and nutrition are "partners" in these crunchy butterscotch cookies.

Cowboy Cookies

1 cup soft shortening or
   margarine
¾ cup brown sugar, packed
¾ cup granulated sugar
2 eggs
1 tsp. vanilla extract
2 cups flour
½ tsp. baking soda

½ tsp. salt
1½ cups quick cooking oatmeal
½ cup coarsely chopped nuts
   or wheat germ
6 ozs. chocolate chips
1 cup raisins

Cream shortening, add sugars and beat well. Add the eggs and vanilla stir to blend well. Add the dry ingredients at one time, mix to blend thoroughly. Last stir in oatmeal, nuts, chocolate chips and raisins. Mix well. Drop by spoonfuls on cookie sheet and bake for 13 – 15 minutes in 350° oven. This dough freezes well and can be sliced later to make fresh cookies. Makes four dozen large cookies.

Low fat:	Use ¾ cup shortening and omit nuts.
Low lactose:	Acceptable
Low sodium:	Omit salt, use unsalted nuts.
Sugar free:	Not acceptable
Calories:	135 per cookie
Protein:	2 gm. per cookie

Peanut butter fans with a "mind for sweets" will like this nourishing bar cookie.

Peanut Butter Bars

¼ cup margarine	1½ cups flour
¼ cup peanut butter	1½ tsp. baking powder
1⅓ cup brown sugar, packed	½ cup chocolate chips
2 eggs	½ cup finely chopped nuts (optional)

Cream margarine and peanut butter. Add brown sugar and mix well. Add both eggs and mix until well blended. Stir in dry ingredients until blended, then chips and nuts. Spread batter in greased and floured 9 inch square pan. Bake at 350° for 30 – 35 minutes. Cool in pan. Cut when cooled into 36 bars.

Low fat:	Acceptable
Low lactose:	Acceptable
Low sodium:	Substitute unsalted peanut butter.
Sugar free:	Not acceptable
Calories:	90 per bar
Protein:	2 gms. per bar

A great way to enjoy fruit and gelatin.

Fluffy Fruit Gelatin

1 cup cooked or canned peaches with syrup
1 package red gelatin (3 ozs.)
1 cup boiling water

Blend fruit with syrup at high speed until smooth. Pour pureed fruit back into measuring cup and add enough syrup or water to make one cup. Dissolve gelatin in boiling water, pour into a bowl (deep enough to whip gelatin later). Stir in fruit puree. Cool. Refrigerate gelatin mixture until it piles softly, but is not firm. With cold beaters, whip the gelatin until foamy and doubled in volume. Refrigerate until firm. Serves six.

Other fruits: Use pears, applesauce or apricots in place of peaches.

Fluffy Fruit Cream: Fold in 1 cup of whipped cream or non-dairy whipped topping after whipping the gelatin. Refrigerate until firm.

Fat free

Lactose free

Low sodium: Acceptable

Sugar free: Use dietetic or unsweetened peaches and
                dietetic gelatin.

Calories: 90 per serving

Protein: 1 gm. per serving

An old standby which is still popular, serve it hot or chilled.

Rice Pudding

1 Tbl. cornstarch
1½ Tbls. granulated sugar
1 beaten egg

1 cup milk
½ cup well cooked rice
½ tsp. vanilla

Blend first three ingredients in saucepan until smooth. Add milk slowly, stirring to mix well. Add rice. Cook over medium heat, stirring constantly until mixture is thickened and comes to a boil. Remove from heat, add vanilla and cool. Sprinkle with cinnamon and nutmeg if desired. Many prefer rice pudding warm. Try it for a new taste treat. Makes three servings.

Low fat: Use low fat milk.

Low lactose: Substitute soy formula for milk.

Low sodium: Acceptable

Sugar free: Acceptable

Calories: 140 per serving

Protein: 6 gms. per serving

A pleasant dessert for those with a "sweet tooth" who cannot drink milk.

Milk-Free Vanilla Pudding

¼ cup sugar   1 egg, beaten
2 Tbls. cornstarch   1 tsp. vanilla
2 cups Isomil or Neomullsoy

Measure sugar and cornstarch into saucepan. Add a little of the soy formula. Stir to dissolve cornstarch, then pour in the rest of the liquid. Add beaten egg. Cook over medium heat until it comes to a boil and is thickened. Add vanilla and cool. Makes four servings.

Maple pudding: Omit vanilla and add ½ tsp. maple flavoring.

Maple-Nut Pudding: Add ¼ to ½ cup chopped walnuts or pecans to cooled pudding.

Coconut Pudding: Add ½ cup coconut. Read the ingredient listing on coconut to be sure it has no lactose added.

Low fat: Acceptable

Lactose free

Low sodium: Acceptable

Sugar free: Omit sugar, add sugar substitute after cooking.

Calories: 159 per serving

Protein: 4 gms. per serving

Chocolate dessert lovers will stand in the aisles for this goodie.

Milk-Free Double Chocolate Pudding

2 squares baking chocolate
   (1 oz. each)
1 Tbl. cornstarch

¼ cup granulated sugar
1 cup non-dairy creamer or
   soy formula
1 tsp. vanilla

Melt chocolate in small pan or on foil. Measure cornstarch and sugar into saucepan. Add part of the creamer and stir until cornstarch dissolves. Add the remainder of the creamer. Cook over medium heat until warm. Stir in chocolate and continue cooking until mixture is thick and comes to a boil. Remove from heat. Blend in vanilla and cool. Makes two servings.

Low fat:	Not acceptable
Low lactose:	Acceptable
Low sodium:	Acceptable
Sugar free:	Not acceptable
Calories:	370 per serving soy formula, 455 with non-dairy creamer.
Protein:	11 gms. per serving with soy formula, 5 gms. with non-dairy creamer.

Imitation ice cream — it's de-lovely, delightful, and delicious.

Super Frozen Delight

1 package instant pudding (chocolate, vanilla, butterscotch, or lemon)

2 cups of chilled Isomil or Neomullsoy
2 cups non-dairy whipped topping

Read the label of pudding mix to see that no milk, or other milk product has been included. Prepare pudding as directed, substituting Isomil or Neomullsoy for milk. Gently fold in whipped topping. Pour into freezer container, cover and freeze until firm, about 3 hours. Makes one quart (eight servings).

Nut Delight: Fold in 1 cup of your favorite chopped nuts with the whipped topping.

Low fat: Acceptable

Low lactose: Acceptable

Low sodium: Acceptable

Sugar free: Not Acceptable

Calories: 133 per serving

Protein: 1 gm. per serving

A speedy answer to the cheesecake — great for the single person.

Individual Cheese Pies

1 Tbl. ricotta cheese
1 Tbl. applesauce (pureed),
   peaches or drained crushed
   pineapple

2 tsps. sugar
sprinkle of cinnamon
one 3 inch sugar cookie (store
   bought)

Blend cheese, fruit, sugar and cinnamon. Spoon over a sugar cookie, turned upside down so the sugar is on the bottom next to the cookie sheet or foil. Bake at 350° for 15 minutes. (The cookie softens as it absorbs the liquid from the fruit-cheese mixture. For a softer treat, lower the oven to 325°.) Serves one.

Low fat:	Use part-skim ricotta cheese and graham or milk crackers.
Low lactose:	Not acceptable
Low sodium:	Acceptable
Sugar free:	Use unsweetened fruit with graham or milk cracker. Omit sugar.
Calories:	85 per pie
Protein:	2 gms. per pie

A quickly made bread, high on the list of nourishing foods.

Banana-Nut Bread

2 eggs
3 medium well ripened bananas,
   cut into chunks
¼ cup of milk
¼ cup oil
1 tsp. vanilla extract
2 cups all purpose flour

¾ cup sugar
1 Tbl. baking powder
½ tsp. baking soda
½ tsp. salt
¼ tsp. nutmeg
½ – 1 cup chopped walnuts,
   pecans or wheat germ

Blend eggs, bananas, milk, oil and vanilla at medium speed until smooth, about 15 seconds. Measure rest of ingredients into a bowl and stir to mix. Make a well in the center of the dry ingredients and pour in banana mixture. Mix just enough to moisten. Add nuts. Spread batter into well greased 9 x 5 x 3 inch loaf pan or 3 small 5 x 3 x 2 inch pans. Bake the bread at 350°, about 1 hour for the large loaf and 35 – 45 minutes for the smaller ones. Makes one large loaf or three small loaves (16 slices).

Low fat:	Omit nuts or wheat germ
Lactose free:	Omit milk, use non-dairy creamer or soy formula.
Low sodium:	Omit salt
Sugar free:	Not acceptable
Calories:	185 per serving
Protein:	3 gms. per slice

A soft delightful dessert made with bread and tasty apples.

Apple Brown Betty

4 cups thinly sliced apples or 1
   can (16 oz.) pie apples, drained
2 cups bread cubes or torn bread
   pieces
½ cup brown sugar, packed

⅛ tsp. ground cinnamon
2 Tbls. margarine
¼ cup hot water

Grease one-quart baking dish. Arrange half of apples on bottom of dish. Follow with half of bread, then half of sugar. Repeat layers. Sprinkle cinnamon over top, cut margarine in pieces and lay them on top, finish by pouring hot water over all. Cover and bake at 350° for 30 minutes, uncover and bake ten minutes longer. Serve warm or chilled. Serves four.

Apple Cheese Betty: Spoon 1 cup ricotta cheese over first layer of apples, bread and sugar. Complete as above.

Low fat:	Use 1 Tbl. margarine
Lactose free:	Use milk-free bread and non-dairy margarine. Omit ricotta cheese.
Low sodium:	Acceptable
Sugar free:	Not acceptable
Calories:	291 per serving; 342 per serving (with cheese)
Protein:	1 gm. per serving; 4 gms. per serving (with cheese)

Delightful as a plain moist cake, or mouth watering when iced with Helen's chocolate frosting.

Adair's Apple Raisin Cake

1¾ cup coarsely chopped apples, or drained canned pie apples, chopped
¾ cup brown sugar, packed
½ cup oil
1 egg, beaten
½ tsp. baking soda
1 tsp. baking powder

½ tsp. salt
1½ cups flour
1 tsp. cinnamon
½ tsp. nutmeg
½ cup raisins, plumed in warm water
½ cup chopped nuts

Measure apples and brown sugar into bowl. Add oil and eggs. Add dry ingredients and mix well. This dough will be stiff.

Add raisins and nuts. Stir to blend. Spread in 8-inch square pan. Bake at 350° for 40 minutes or until top springs back when touched. May be frozen. Makes 16 pieces.

Contributed by Adair Luciani

Low fat: Use ¼ cup oil.

Lactose free

Low sodium: Omit salt, use unsalted nuts.

Sugar free: Not acceptable

Calories: 200 per piece

Protein: 3 gms. per piece

A good, fast-cooked icing.

Helen's Soft Chocolate Frosting

½ cup white sugar
½ cup brown sugar
3 heaping Tbls. cocoa
3 heaping Tbls. cornstarch

1 cup milk
3 Tbls. margarine

Mix first four ingredients together in saucepan until well blended. Gradually add milk. Add margarine. Cook over medium heat, stirring constantly until thick and smooth. (You may need to remove from heat occasionally to prevent sticking or lumping.) Ice cake while the frosting is still warm. Ices two 9 inch layers, (serving 16 people). Recipe can easily be cut in half for a single layer cake or cupcakes.

Contributed by Helen Monahan

Low fat: Use 1 Tbl. margarine

Low lactose: Substitute water for milk. Use non-dairy margarine.

Low sodium: Acceptable

Sugar free: Not acceptable

Calories: 91 per serving

Protein: 1 gm. per serving

Nutritional Formulas and Preparations Commonly Available

Product Name/ Company	Sizes Available	Serving Size
Liquids: Ensure*/Ross	8 ounce can 32 ounce can	8 oz.
Isomil*/Ross	13 oz. can conc. 8, 32 oz. can dilute	10 oz.
Meritene/Doyle	10 oz. can	10 oz.
Mull-Soy*t/Syntex	13 oz. can conc.	10 oz.
Neo-Mull-Soy*t/ Syntex	14 oz. can conc.	10 oz.
Prosobeet/Mead Johnson	13 oz. can conc.	10 oz.
Sustacal/Mead Johnson	12 oz. can	12 oz.
Powders:** Instant Breakfast, Carnation	Ctn. of 6, 1.26 oz. pkts.	1 packet
Lolactene*/Doyle	Ctn. of 6, 2 oz. pkts.	1 packet
Meritene/Doyle	1 lb. can	1.14 oz. measure
Suscatal/Doyle	Ctn. of 4, 1.9 oz. pkts.	1 packet

*Recipes available from the manufacturer
t Available where infant formulas are sold
**Calorie and protein content when prepared as directed on the package

Approximate content per serv.		Special Characteristics	Flavors Available
Calories	Protein Grams		
250	8.8	Lactose and milk free, contains soy protein	Vanilla Black Walnut
200	6.0	Lactose and milk free, contains soy protein	
300	18.0	Contains milk	Vanilla, Chocolate, Egg-nog
200	8.5	Milk and lactose free, contains soy flour	
200	5.0	Milk and lactose free, contains soy protein	
200	7.5	contains soy protein	
360	21.7	Low lactose, contains soy protein and milk	Vanilla, Chocolate
290	16.0	Contains milk and soy protein, high lactose	6 flavors
227	15.0	Low lactose milk	Vanilla
277	18.0	Contains milk, high lactose	Vanilla, Chocolate, Egg-nog
360	21.7	Contains milk, high lactose	Vanilla, Chocolate

Cookbooks To Consider

The following books are inexpensive, easy to use and readily available in discount or bookstores.

Afterwork Cookbook: Designed for those who prefer good food but have less time available for cooking. Better Homes and Gardens, Meredith Corp., Des Moines, Iowa, 1974. $4.95.

American Heart Association Cookbook: Recipes designed for low saturated fat cooking. Available from local American Heart Association units, $2.50 (paperback).

Blender Cookbook: A standby for those who often use blenders. Better Homes and Gardens, Meredith Corp., Des Moines, Iowa, 1971. $3.95.

Cookbook for Boys and Girls: Helpful when children need to do some of the cooking. Betty Crocker, Golden Press, New York, Western Publication Co., Inc., Racine, Wisconsin, 1977. $2.95.

Good and Easy Cookbook: Basic cookbook featuring easy presentation. Betty Crocker, Golden Press, New York, Western Publication Co., Inc., Racine, Wisconsin, 1977. $2.95.

Hamburger Cookbook: Those who need soft meats will find a variety of basic choices here. Betty Crocker, Golden Press, New York, Western Publication Co., Inc., Racine, Wisconsin, 1977. $2.95 (paperback).

Microwave Cooking: Basic guide to microwave cooking. Better Homes and Gardens, Meredith Corp., Des Moines, Iowa, 1976. $3.95.

Recipes for A Small Planet: Helpful for vegetarian cooks. Ellen B. Ewald, Ballentine Books, New York, 1973, $2.50.

The Soft Foods Cookbook: Well-written guide to preparing and planning soft and blended diets. Anne S. Chamberlin, Doubleday and Co., Garden City, New York, 1973. $5.95.

Notes

Notes

Recipe Index